MW00647660

PAUL E. MILLER

LOVE

WALKED

AMONG

US

Lydia Leggett and
Michele Bennett Walton

a global discipling mission

2019
seeJesus Press

By Lydia Leggett and Michele Bennett Walton

seeJesus is a global discipling mission helping the church see and reflect the life, death, and resurrection of Christ through discipleship resources and training.

seeJesus
P.O. Box 197
Telford, PA 18969
Phone: 215.721.3113
Fax: 215.721.6535
info@seeJesus.net
www.seeJesus.net

Project Manager: Michele Bennett Walton
Copyeditor: Sherri Hughes
Typesetter and Layout Design: Pat Reinheimer
Cover Design: Mary Ann Martin

ISBN: 978-1-941178-29-4

CONTENTS

Foreword   5
Preface   7
12-Week Reading Plan   8

Introduction: Who Is Jesus?   9

Part 1:
LOVE SHOWS COMPASSION
1. A Mind Full of Someone Else: *Love Looks and Acts*   13
2. Looking Shapes the Heart: *Learning How to See People*   17
3. "I Know What's Best for You": *Judging Blocks Compassion*   21
4. "I'm Better Than You": *Self-Righteousness Blocks Compassion*   25
5. "This Is What You Should Do": *Legalism Blocks Compassion*   29
6. The Golden Rule: *Incarnation Leads to Compassion*   33

Part 2:
LOVE SPEAKS THE TRUTH
7. A Time to Speak Up: *Balancing Compassion with Honesty*   39
8. Honest Anger: *A Compassionate Warning to Others*   43
9. A Time to Shut Up: *Balancing Honesty with Compassion*   47
10. "I Know How Hard It Is; I Do the Same Thing":   51
    Being Honest Without Being Judgmental

Part 3:
LOVE DEPENDS ON GOD
11. The Secret to Love: *Dependence on God*   57
12. Saying "No" to Someone You Love: 61
    Compassionately Responding to Demands

13. Saying "No" to Self-Gratification: *Love That Is Pure*   65
14. Saying "Yes" to Gentle Intrusion: *Love Brings Light into Darkness*   69

Part 4:
LOVE IS ENERGIZED BY FAITH

15. Faith Empowers Love: *Where Can I Find the Energy to Love?*   75
16. Faith Means Losing Control: *Going to God with Our Needs*   79
17. The Intimate Stranger: *Weaving a Fabric of Love*   83
18. Oneness: *Love Leads to Intimacy*   87

Part 5:
LOVE MOVES THROUGH DEATH INTO LIFE

19. The Way of Humility: *Love Takes the Lower Place*   93
20. Facing Sadness: *When Love Leads to Grief*   97
21. A Symphony of Love: *Love Under Pressure*   101
22. His Life for Ours: *The Cost of Love*   105
23. The Birth of Hope: *The End of Love's Journey*   107
24. Opening the Door: *What Do We Do with Jesus?*   109

About the Authors   111

FOREWORD

Dear Reader,

I'm delighted you've decided to immerse yourself in *Love Walked Among Us*. It was my first book, and it's still my favorite. That little story I begin the book with, of my wife Jill asking me, "Do you love me?" was the spark behind my whole discovery of the person of Jesus. I hope these three things happen as you study the person of Jesus:

First, I hope you learn to love in new ways. I still remember the day in March 1991 when I noticed the pattern of Jesus looking at people and then compared that with how inattentive I could be with Jill and others. That insight led to my great epiphany, mentioned in the book, that I was more efficient than Jesus! Of course, my efficiency reflected my shortcoming—how I didn't slow down and look at and value people. I hope, as you study, that you look at Jesus.

Second, I hope that you begin to encounter Jesus' beauty as you burrow into his life. I don't think I can explain how it happens, but I suspect as you read you'll notice me, at times, filled with wonder. I'm still often stunned by his beauty, how complex his love is, how other-centered he is.

Third, I hope that our attention to Jesus' relationships and patterns of love will help you experience an embodied Jesus. Particularly if you've grown up in the church, you'll know about Jesus as Savior but not as a Person. I want you to be able to feel him, to experience him, to pick up his cadences. I can spot my wife a block away just by her walk. I hope you begin to spot Jesus.

Finally, if you are not a believer or have left the faith, weary because you saw one too many Christians who didn't reflect Jesus, I hope this book begins a path back to the very heart of the Christian faith—the person of Jesus. He is altogether lovely!

Enjoy his beauty,
Paul E. Miller

October 2019

PREFACE

The purpose of this discussion guide, a companion to *Love Walked Among Us*, is to help us learn to love by looking at Jesus.

Love sounds simple, but most of us can recall a moment when reality dawned, and we wondered suddenly: do I even know what "love" means? How can I possibly love _____? *Love Walked Among Us* was born out of author Paul Miller's struggle to answer similar questions.

We will have a two-fold primary focus throughout this discussion guide: Jesus and love. Before you begin, take a few minutes to pray and reflect on the following question: whom do I struggle to love? Confess your struggle to God, then keep your eyes and heart open to see where the Spirit may be at work.

Much of what you will be encouraged to do in the following pages won't sound spiritual. *Look, feel, act*—these could be instructions from a self-help book. But the truth is that we don't have the power in and of ourselves to sustain the movements of love. We can muscle through looking and entering into someone else's life for a day or two, but we can't love for the long haul without the power of God's Spirit.

We'll do the easy work of walking you, step by step, through the pages of the book. You will do the harder work of searching your heart and listening to the Spirit. But the Spirit will do the miracle of transforming your mind, heart, and relationships.

We are grateful for the contributions of Timothy Geiger, Matt Mitchell, Jim Arcieri, and Larry Schmidt, who deeply dove into the work of love with their own groups and gave us permission to use some of their questions.

12-WEEK READING PLAN

10/6   Week 1: Introduction and Chapter 1 — KEEGAN

10/20   Week 2: Chapters 2-3 — SAM

11/3   Week 3: Chapters 4-5 — SARAH

11/10 Dinner
        Week 4: Chapters 6-7

Week 5: Chapters 8-9

Week 6: Chapters 10-11

Week 7: Chapters 12-13

Week 8: Chapters 14-15

Week 9: Chapters 16-17

Week 10: Chapters 18-19

Week 11: Chapters 20-21

Week 12: Chapters 22-24

Matthew - Tax collector, well educated, can read people
  - eye witness account
Mark - account of Peter, fast-paced + passionate, impact of Jesus
Luke - doctor, travels w/ Paul, based on eyewitness testimonies
  - compassion for the powerless
John - intimate friend of Jesus, up-close glimpses of Him

[Introduction]

WHO IS JESUS?

1. Paul Miller had to forget what he knew—or thought he knew—about Jesus in order to discover him as a real person. Discuss which of these false images of Jesus you need to forget:

   - A nit-picking Jesus who cares about the letter and not the spirit of the law
   - A preoccupied Jesus who is too busy with his work to notice specific needs or minister to individual people
   - A dispassionate Jesus who executes God's will without experiencing or expressing emotion
   - A mythological Jesus who shaped the culture we live in but not the actual world
   - Something else? _____

Don't think of Jesus as a person
Hebrews 4 - Great High priest who experienced temptation
Can empathize with our weakness
is intimate and close

"Which person in the Bible would you most like to meet"

2. When Paul's wife Jill asked him three times if he loved her, he went to bed angrily compiling a mental list of ways he proved his love. Why did Paul respond that way? What did Jill actually mean?

He thought Jill was saying he didn't do enough for her - that actions + service are how you prove love
Jill meant - why do you love me?

3. Consider the people who have modeled love for you. In what ways were these models positive? How were they negative?

Caroline Nichols - demonstrated sacrificial love
- negative because it made it easy to put her on a pedastal look to her for comfort
She is limited + imperfect

4. We never struggle to love people in the abstract; we struggle to love the unique, flesh-and-blood people God has placed in our lives. Prayerfully identify one person you struggle to love well and write that name here: Kayla .

5. What prevents you from loving the person named above? Do you get overwhelmed by his or her needs? Are you too busy judging him or her to reach out? Do you feel trapped or used? Take a few minutes and confess your struggle to God, asking him to use this study to teach you how to love this person.

Overwhelmed by her needs
Feel diminished + broken trust that hasn't been addressed
Am embarassed at times

How do you decipher if someone is a good person to be friends w/ invest time in?
I feel a sense of commitment + obligation to many friends and don't know if it is rightly placed

Part 1

LOVE SHOWS COMPASSION

Chapter 1

A MIND FULL OF SOMEONE ELSE

LOVE LOOKS AND ACTS

1. The first story about the widow of Nain includes details that are easy to skim over. Reread it slowly, visualizing the scene. What strikes you about Jesus? How does he show love?

   The Lord saw
   His heart went out to her
   He said "don't cry"
   He went up + touched the bier + raised the dead son

2. Paul Miller emphasizes that *first* Jesus looks at the widow, *then* he feels compassion. Discuss why this sequence matters.

   He doesn't feel without knowing

3. How does it make you feel when Jesus tells the widow, "Don't cry"? (Keep in mind that if you object to something you see Jesus doing, it may be helpful to ask the Spirit to show you why.)

Comfort
It's going to be okay
Hope for the future

4. Celebrate a situation from the past week in which the Spirit enabled you to love by following Jesus' pattern of looking, feeling compassion, and helping. Share with the group as you feel comfortable.

Processing Faith w/ Jason
Look - saw that He was upset on the phone
Help - listened + asked questions
         Shared hope + encouragement

5. Now identify one situation from the past week in which you struggled to love another person. What happened? How could Jesus' 3-step pattern also help you to love in this circumstance?

Anxiety + freezing up
I literally wouldn't look at Jason or
feel compassion towards him
I was too wrapped up in my own emotions

6. On page 28, Paul says, "Jesus' tenderness suggested to me a new, less 'efficient,' way of relating." In which areas of your life do efficiency and order keep you from loving people? Be specific.

Just want + jump to solution + move on
Don't see walking through the mess
itself as beneficial but obstacle

7. Paul writes, "Jesus has shown us how to love: Look, feel, and then help" (28). Pray about the situation you identified in question 5. How is the Spirit leading you to love this person differently?

8. What did the Spirit help you see about either Jesus or yourself through this lesson?

Jesus _saw_ people and was intimately involved with them
He wasn't stoic but able to be emotionally affected
Emotions aren't always manipulative + untrustworthy

Chapter 2

LOOKING SHAPES
THE HEART

LEARNING HOW TO SEE PEOPLE

1. This chapter explores how love begins with looking. Which specific situations in your life tempt you to look away? (Examples: when my kids are moody; when I've had an argument with my spouse; when my coworker needs help again.)

2. We look away for a reason. What does looking away do for you in the situation(s) mentioned above? What would looking require you to do?

3. What similarities do you see between how the Good Samaritan helps the wounded man and how Jesus loves the widow of Nain?

4. Imagine you are the lost son from the parable. Describe how you feel when you see your father running toward you.

5. With the emotions of the lost son still fresh in your mind, try to absorb the truth of the parable: God ran to *you* in Christ! (See Romans 8:32, 2 Corinthians 5:21, 1 John 4:10.) Take a moment to thank God for his cherishing love.

6. As you begin to look at others more intentionally, what changes do you notice in yourself?

7. What if looking at someone doesn't produce compassion? Reread page 31 and ask God to grant you "healthy" eyes (Matthew 6:22) to see as he sees.

8. What did the Spirit help you see about either Jesus or yourself through this lesson?

Chapter 3

"I KNOW WHAT'S BEST FOR YOU"

JUDGING BLOCKS COMPASSION

1. Imagine you are walking with Jesus and the disciples when they encounter the blind man. How do you respond to him?

2. How does Jesus love the blind man in this story? How does he love the disciples? "Jesus lowers himself in order to care, while the disciples elevate themselves in order to judge" (39). How does this statement impact you?

3. Judging destroys community, but compassion creates it. Why? Reflect on one example, either positive or negative, from your own life.

4. Paul Miller writes, "Compassion affects us. Maybe that's why we judge so quickly—it keeps us from being infected by other people's problems" (39). What "infections" does passing judgment on others protect you from?

5. In which relationships in your life does judging block compassion?

6. "When we stop judging, we rest from the incessant work of analyzing others. We don't need to figure out what's wrong with people—that's God's job. Our job is to try to understand" (46). Take a few minutes to reflect on how God might be offering you rest.

7. How is the Spirit leading you to relate to others differently?

8. What did the Spirit help you see about either Jesus or yourself through this lesson?

Chapter 4

"I'M BETTER THAN YOU"

SELF-RIGHTEOUSNESS BLOCKS COMPASSION

1. Get in touch with your inner Pharisee by filling in the blanks:

   "God, I thank you that I am not like _____
   (*a group of people that drives you crazy*) or even like _____
   (*one particular person who drives you crazy*). I _____
   (*something good you do that those people don't do*)."

2. In what ways is God pinpointing self-righteousness in you?

3. Reflect on the parable of the prodigal son. How are you like the older brother?

4. Simon judges Jesus before the sinful woman walks through the door. How do we see this? Why might he have done so?

5. What strikes you most about Jesus' interactions with the woman at Simon's house? If you were in Jesus' place in the scene, what would you have done differently?

6. How does Jesus love both the woman and Simon? How does his honesty correspond with his compassion?

7. Paul Miller writes, "The better we think we are, the less we can love" (55). How does realizing we don't have it all together free us to love others? Discuss as a group.

8. Consider one specific relationship or situation in your life in which self-righteousness blocks compassion. Briefly review Chapter 4, looking for insights that help you make room for compassion in that relationship or situation. Make a note of that here.

9. Write a short response to the words of your "inner Pharisee" in question 1. What truths does he or she need to hear?

10. What did the Spirit help you see about either Jesus or yourself through this lesson?

Chapter 5

"THIS IS WHAT YOU SHOULD DO"

LEGALISM BLOCKS COMPASSION

1. Try out Paul Miller's exercise on page 60: "...take a notepad to work or family gathering and jot down your thoughts—good and bad—about others. Every criticism, every fear, every compassion, every jealousy. Be honest about what you are really thinking. Then shred it." What did you learn about yourself? Where is the real problem in your life?

2. What is the false gospel of legalism?

3. "Good and true things blind the legalist," which can make legalism difficult to self-diagnose. Discuss with the group some of your personal (extra-biblical) rules by answering the questions below:

    a. People shouldn't _____ . (Examples: waste money, talk loudly, be shy, etc.)
    b. People must _____ . (Examples: vote in a certain way, exercise regularly, etc.)

4. "[Legalism] systematizes judging, eliminating gray areas so we don't have to think about love" (57). How do you use legalism to make sense of life?

5. Reflect on what rules or tendency toward legalism you notice in other people. Then prayerfully consider if you struggle with the same things.

6. How does Jesus deal with legalism?

7. Do you naturally relate to Mary or Martha in Luke 10:38-42? How does Jesus love Mary? How does he love Martha?

8. Read Luke 11:37-43. Ask the Father to show you how you "clean the outside of the cup" but leave the inside a mess. (Don't forget to ask him to help you clean the inside, too!)

9. What did the Spirit help you see about either Jesus or yourself through this lesson?

Chapter 6

THE GOLDEN RULE

INCARNATION LEADS TO COMPASSION

1. What is the opposite of judging, self-righteousness, and legalism? (In other words, what do we call the act of slowing down to love someone, stepping into their shoes?)

2. Consider a time when someone—a parent, a friend, a spouse, a pastor—stepped into your shoes and "incarnated" with you. What did that feel like?

3. Paul Miller recounts how he encountered little beliefs—frugality and efficiency, in his example—that threatened to prevent him from showing compassion to his daughter (68). What "little beliefs" can block your compassion?

4. Discuss how the Golden Rule turns self-awareness on its head (69). What two things does it require us to do? In what order?

5. Is there someone in your life who needs the equivalent of a varsity wrestling jacket? Look closely and prayerfully at that person and his or her needs. Ask the Spirit for help in identifying how you can incarnate with him or her.

6. Be careful of taking a good rule—incarnation—and turning it into legalism! How does Jesus "shape his love to the person"?

7. Review how Jesus asks the blind man questions in Mark 10:47-52. How can asking questions of people help us to incarnate with them?

8. Jesus incarnated with us in coming to earth (Hebrews 2:14), and he does that now in interceding for us (Romans 8:34). Having reflected on how difficult it is to incarnate with others, how do these truths impact you? Share with the group as you are comfortable.

9. What did the Spirit help you see about either Jesus or yourself through this lesson?

10. What have you learned about compassion in the first part of this book? How is that impacting your life?

Part 2

LOVE SPEAKS THE TRUTH

Chapter 7

A TIME TO SPEAK UP

BALANCING COMPASSION WITH HONESTY

1. Why do we complain to friends about issues we have with others? At Simon's house, what does Jesus do instead?

2. What is beautiful about Jesus' honesty?

3. Do you typically confront people, or do you shy away from speaking honestly? Jot down one example. How is this like or unlike Jesus' pattern of confronting?

4. Have you ever had a relationship "get weird" because of a lack of honesty? Describe what happened.

5. On page 78, Paul Miller writes: "[Jesus] told his followers to have an honesty that moves toward people." Read Matthew 18:15 and reflect on what this means.

6. Paul writes, "Jesus always uses his power to help people" (80). What other stories in the Gospels show Jesus using prominence to aid the "lower" people around him? Discuss as a group.

7. What hypocritical masks do you tend to wear?

8. Reflect on a time you resisted the temptation to manipu-
   late another person. Describe the situation, what you were
   tempted to say, and what you actually said. How did it affect
   you and/or the other person to speak honestly like Jesus?

9. If you threw out all hidden agendas, manipulation, and gos-
   siping—what one relationship in your life would change
   most? Why? How? Pray as the Spirit leads.

10. What did the Spirit help you see about either Jesus or your-
    self through this lesson?

Chapter 8

HONEST ANGER

A COMPASSIONATE WARNING TO OTHERS

1. Do you typically suppress or express your anger? Explain.

2. How do you feel about the fact that Jesus gets angry? Discuss as a group.

3. When, according to Paul Miller, does Jesus get irritated? Why is that okay?

4. What happens to Jesus' compassion when he's angry? (See the story of the man with the shriveled hand for an example.)

5. Paul says, "Our irritation, rightly used to act in love, can fuel a few honest words, which in turn can help people" (92). How can Jesus' example shape our own tendency toward irritation?

6. Recall a recent incident in which you were angry. How was your anger like and unlike Jesus' rage in the temple?

7. How do you respond when someone else is treated unjustly?

8. When you are treated unjustly, how does Jesus respond?

9. Paul writes, "[Jesus'] anger is powerful, controlled, and creative" (96). Reflect on what is both beautiful and remarkable about Jesus' anger.

10. What things in your life do you hold tightly? Notice how these things can tempt you toward anger that is not "a compassionate warning to others." Pray as the Spirit leads.

11. What did the Spirit help you see about either Jesus or yourself through this lesson?

Chapter 9

A TIME TO SHUT UP

Balancing Honesty with Compassion

1. Paul Miller explains that Jesus' honest confrontations were always "for" others (98). What does that mean? Where do you see this in the Gospels? Discuss as a group.

2. Describe a situation in which you tried to be honest but realized, too late, that you should have been quiet. What happened?

3. Now describe a time when you held back what you wanted to say in order to love someone. How was that different from the situation you described in question 2?

4. Why is it hard to let someone else have the last word? Why is it hard for us to be quiet?

5. Read Matthew 10:34. Why is this a difficult passage for the American culture? What does it unmask in our lives? How might you have a commitment to peace that shrinks from "speaking the truth in love"? Discuss as a group.

6. Reflect on a time when you used sweeping generalizations —"always" or "never" language—with someone. How did your words affect the situation? What specific and helpful examples might you have shared instead?

7. Read Matthew 18:15 in context, starting with verse 21 and reading through verse 35. How does being forgiven enable us to forgive?

8. What did the Spirit help you see about either Jesus or yourself through this lesson?

Chapter 10

"I KNOW HOW HARD IT IS; I DO THE SAME THING"

BEING HONEST WITHOUT BEING JUDGMENTAL

1. Read Jesus' instructions in Matthew 7:3-5. What is "Beam Research"? How is it related to Jesus' Golden Rule?

2. Think about one relationship in your life that feels strained and do some Beam Research. What specific things does this person do that bother you? Prayerfully consider how you do the same things and note them here. Or, even better, go ask him or her: "If there was one thing about me you could change to improve our relationship, what would it be?" (Make sure you listen carefully to the response.)

3. Sometimes we simply have not done the same thing. How can you love in honesty without being judgmental in those times? Discuss as a group.

4. What is our instinctive reaction when dealing with enemies? How does Jesus instruct us to love people who won't accept honest words: our enemies?

5. Read Matthew 5:38-48. Do you have anyone in your life who might qualify as an enemy? (The label "enemy" is not intended to malign the person but to offer you instruction in loving him or her more effectively.)

6. How might you begin to love the person you mentioned in question 5 "without words," as Paul Miller explains on page 111?

7. Reflect on how God has loved you, personally, when you were his enemy.

8. Is there anything the Spirit is leading you to do? Make a note of that here.

9. What did the Spirit help you see about either Jesus or yourself through this lesson?

10. What have you learned about honesty in the second part of this book? How is that impacting your life?

Part 3

LOVE DEPENDS ON GOD

Chapter 11

THE SECRET
TO LOVE

DEPENDENCE ON GOD

1. Read John 7:1-9. Put yourself in Jesus' brothers' shoes and tell this story from their point of view. What were your concerns about Jesus? What did he seem oblivious to? Try to capture the pride of those of us who love to give free advice.

2. What do you think Jesus means in John 5:30 when he says, "By myself I can do nothing"? What implications does this have for Jesus' relationship with his Father? For our relationship with Jesus? Discuss as a group.

3. While Jesus appears to be in bondage, how is he actually free? What is he free from?

4. In what areas are you willful (wanting your own way)? Ask the Spirit for help in answering this question, but also don't be afraid to ask your spouse, parent, sibling, or a close friend.

5. How have you felt trapped by other people's agendas? What would it look like to say no to them and yes to your Father? Share with the group as you feel comfortable.

6. Paul Miller writes, "Compassion and honesty, the visible first and second floors of love, rest on the foundation of dependence on God" (120). What does this mean? How have you seen this play out in your own life?

7. Reflect on one of the areas of willfulness you mentioned in question 4. What would happen if you slowed down this week and, like Jesus, surrendered your will to God in this area? What would change?

8. Is there something you need to stop asking someone else to do and start asking God to do? Make a note of that here.

9. Paul writes, "Prayer gives us direction about how to love" (123). Where do you need direction about how to love?

10. What did the Spirit help you see about either Jesus or yourself through this lesson?

Chapter 12

SAYING "NO" TO SOMEONE YOU LOVE

COMPASSIONATELY RESPONDING TO DEMANDS

1. What did you notice about how Jesus says no to his mother?

2. We tend to think that love means saying yes to every need or demand that comes along. What does Jesus' example teach us? Discuss as a group.

3. How do you typically respond to the demands of those you love? How are your responses like or unlike Jesus' responses to his mother?

4. How did Jesus respond to the strong-willed people around him in the story of the wedding at Cana? (See John 2:1-11.)

5. Think of a time when you had a hard time saying no because, like Jeff, you were afraid of appearing selfish. Would you respond differently now? How?

6. Describe a time you felt pressure to "do more." How could dependence on God protect you from others' demands?

7. How did dependence on God ultimately shape Mary's relationship with Jesus? (See page 135.)

8. What did the Spirit help you see about either Jesus or yourself through this lesson?

Chapter 13

SAYING "NO" TO SELF-GRATIFICATION

LOVE THAT IS PURE

1. Paul Miller writes, "...what sucks me in repulses Jesus" (141). What does he mean? What kinds of things do you find life in, instead of in Jesus? Discuss as a group.

2. In what specific areas are you tempted by self-gratification? How does self-gratification impact your ability to love others? (Be specific!)

3. Read John 2:13-22. Why would it be wrong for Jesus to do a sign?

4. Give an example of a time you were tempted to say or do something to make yourself look good in front of other people. How is Jesus different from you?

5. Read John 15:12-14. Jesus saying no to self meant he said yes to suffering and death for us, in obedience to the Father. What strikes you about this act of love?

6. How has saying no to self led to suffering in your own life?

7. Paul writes, "...if our love depends on how the other person loves us, then we have a business deal, not love" (144). Where is God calling you to love? What might you need to say no to in your life today?

8. What did the Spirit help you see about either Jesus or yourself through this lesson?

Chapter 14

SAYING "YES" TO GENTLE INTRUSION

Love Brings Light into Darkness

1. Reflect on a time you moved away from someone in their sin or selfishness.

2. Now think about a time someone moved toward you in your suffering or in your selfishness. What happened to you? To the other person?

3. "When we love, we get dirty" (150). What does Paul Miller mean by this? Discuss as a group.

4. Are you willing to get dirty? If you aren't—or if you feel hesitant to say yes—take some time to pray and ask God to work in your heart. Record that prayer below so you can watch how he answers it in the weeks and months to come.

5. Think of some examples in Scripture where Jesus physically touched someone. What does his touch say about God's heart?

6. Read Luke 8:40-55 and Mark 5:30, 32. Notice the specific ways Jesus loves each person. What does he do with the woman in the crowd? With Jairus? With Jairus's daughter?

7. Where might God be calling you to gently intrude in someone else's life to bring light into darkness?

8. What did the Spirit help you see about either Jesus or yourself through this lesson?

9. What have you learned about dependence on God in the third part of this book? How is that impacting your life?

LOVE IS ENERGIZED BY FAITH

Chapter 15

FAITH EMPOWERS LOVE

WHERE CAN I FIND THE ENERGY TO LOVE?

1. Miller writes, "The hardest part of love is not, 'How do I love?';
   it's wanting to love in the first place, and then having the
   energy to do it" (161). Can you recall a time when you knew
   what loving someone would require of you and you chose not
   to do it? What stopped you? (Be as specific as you can.)

2. How does your life sometimes show that you have faith in
   something other than Jesus? Discuss as a group.

3. Read Mark 6:30-44 and John 6:22-40, 48-51 and imagine you are Jesus. Crowds of people have swarmed you. You're exhausted. And you'd like to get away for a few hours with your close friends. What would you have done when the crowds found you again? What does Jesus do? What does Mark 6:34 say that Jesus felt?

4. Paul Miller writes, "Love begins, not with loving, but with being loved. Being loved gives you the freedom and the resources to love" (165). Spend some time in prayer, examining your heart before the Lord and answering this question: do I have the freedom and resources to love?

5. In the next paragraph, Paul adds: "Faith at its simplest is receiving love..." (165). If you found yourself lacking in the freedom or resources to love, ask God to grant you more faith. Faith in God provides the energy for love.

6. Read Matthew 11:28. How is it possible to love the beat-up, the dirty, and our enemies? (See page 168.)

7. In what ways have you wanted a breakfast-making "Messiah for me" instead of depending on Jesus as your source of life (167)?

8. Read John 6:53. What would it be like to instead feed on Jesus as the bread of life?

9. What did the Spirit help you see about either Jesus or yourself through this lesson?

Chapter 16

FAITH MEANS LOSING CONTROL

GOING TO GOD WITH OUR NEEDS

1. How did Jesus surprise the disciples in Luke 5:4-11 and Mark 4:39-41? How did he "disrupt their categories"? Discuss as a group.

2. Paul Miller writes, "Following Jesus means losing control" (174). What does this mean, and how does it relate to love? (See Matthew 14:25-32 for help.)

3. Think of a time you stopped looking at Jesus and instead focused on your circumstances. How did you begin to sink? Share with the group as you feel comfortable.

4. How has Jesus surprised you when you have kept your eyes on him in the midst of a storm? Share with the group as you feel comfortable.

5. Reread Mark 8:14-21. What made Jesus so upset? What does Jesus want from us? What does Jesus want for us?

6. Why does faith feel foolish?

7. Think of a situation in your life in which you have been behaving as though Jesus is powerless to help. With that situation in mind, fill in the blanks in the following sentences: Jesus only makes bread when _____ . He won't

_____ .

8. How can you find the energy for love in light of this chapter?

9. What did the Spirit help you see about either Jesus or yourself through this lesson?

Chapter 17

THE INTIMATE STRANGER

WEAVING A FABRIC OF LOVE

1. Read John 4:1-42. What is this Samaritan woman like?

2. How does Jesus engage her in conversation? How does he disrupt normal social categories? Discuss as a group.

3. How does Jesus love the woman? What cultural and spiritual walls does he break down?

4. How does Jesus balance his compassion with honesty in talking with her?

5. In loving people, do you tend to favor being compassionate or being honest? Share an example.

6. How does this story of Jesus with the Samaritan woman help you see how to balance compassion and honesty?

7. The disciples return with food, but Jesus is no longer hungry (John 4:31-35). Why?

8. Paul Miller quotes Napoleon, "Everything in [Jesus] astonishes me. His spirit overawes me, and his will confounds me" (192). In what ways has Jesus astonished you in this chapter? In this study of love?

9. What did the Spirit help you see about either Jesus or yourself through this lesson?

Chapter 18

ONENESS

LOVE LEADS TO INTIMACY

1. Recount a time in which you have experienced true intimacy. What did you do or say? What did the other person do or say? How did you feel?

2. Paul Miller describes oneness as "a state of pure and constant compassion devoid of selfishness" (194). What does that mean? Why does oneness elude us? Discuss as a group.

3. What is the relationship between oneness and joy?

4. Read John 17. In what ways does Jesus indicate he is one with his Father?

5. Typically speaking, what is the goal of your love? What is the goal of Jesus' love?

6. Is there any area in your life where you want to reach out to another person but—like Isabelle's mom—find yourself saying, "I just can't"? Pray and ask God to show you your pride, draw you to himself, and enable you to actively love that person.

7. What struck you most about intimacy in this chapter? How can you live in light of it this week?

8. What did the Spirit help you see about either Jesus or yourself through this lesson?

9. What have you learned about faith in the fourth part of this book? How is that impacting your life?

Part 5

LOVE MOVES THROUGH DEATH INTO LIFE

Chapter 19

THE WAY OF HUMILITY

LOVE TAKES THE LOWER PLACE

1. Recall a time when you saw another person willingly take the lower place. What was unusual about his or her actions? What happened as a result?

2. Henri Nouwen sensed that success was putting his soul in danger. (See page 205.) Recall a time in which your success drew you away from God and others. How did this success ultimately impact your life? Share as you feel comfortable.

3. According to Paul Miller, why are we "allergic to the lower place" (209)? How does Jesus actively choose the lowest place?

4. Read Mark 9:33-35 and Matthew 18:2-5. Who does Jesus point to as an example of the lower place? What does he mean?

5. Do you agree with Nouwen's assessment on page 208 that power is an easy substitute for the hard task of love? Why or why not? Discuss as a group.

6. How does Jesus turn things upside down in Matthew 20:22-28?

7. Paul writes, "We need faith to believe that God will take care of us when others don't" (213). How does humility require faith?

8. Why is the lower place safe?

9. What did the Spirit help you see about either Jesus or yourself through this lesson?

Chapter 20

FACING SADNESS

WHEN LOVE LEADS TO GRIEF

1. How does rejection feel?

2. What strikes you most about knowing Jesus experienced the pain of rejection?

3. When we are sad, whom are we usually thinking about? In Luke 19:41-44, whom is Jesus thinking about on the road to Jerusalem? What does this show you?

4. Reflect upon a time you were hurt. What happened? How did you feel? What did you do? Share as you feel comfortable.

5. Now consider Jesus. As Paul Miller writes, "When he is hurt, he feels sad; when others are hurt, he gets mad. Because he is bound to the Father and not to his own feelings, he feels no bitterness or self-pity" (219). How does Jesus' example instruct you? How does it free you?

6. In what way(s) is sadness a pure response to evil? How can good sadness help us love like Jesus?

7. Read John 12:25-28. What clues does this passage give about Jesus' struggle?

8. Are you feeling depression or anger over a difficult situation in your life? Review this chapter briefly, and prayerfully consider whether sadness is a more faithful response. Note anything the Spirit brings to mind as you pray.

9. What did the Spirit help you see about either Jesus or yourself through this lesson?

Chapter 21

A SYMPHONY OF LOVE

LOVE UNDER PRESSURE

1. Paul Miller writes, "It's relatively easy to love when things are going the way we want. But when the pressure mounts, most of us forget about love and think only about ourselves" (223). How has this been true in your life?

2. How do we typically handle suffering, especially unjust suffering? Discuss as a group.

3. In each phase of Jesus' final few hours, we see him love. Which interaction stands out to you most? Why?

4. How does Jesus love the disciples and Malchus in the Garden of Gethsemane?

5. How do we see Jesus love Pilate? How does he love those who nail him to the cross?

6. Watching Jesus die on the cross, the centurion admits, "Surely this man was the Son of God" (Mark 15:39). What has studying the love of Jesus revealed to you? How have you seen Jesus as the Son of God? Discuss as a group.

7. Where are you under pressure? Who is God calling you to love in that situation?

8. What did the Spirit help you see about either Jesus or yourself through this lesson?

Chapter 22

HIS LIFE FOR OURS

THE COST OF LOVE

1. Share an example, large or small, of a time someone graciously substituted himself or herself for you—perhaps by paying your debt, taking your punishment, or doing your difficult task. How did this make you feel? What benefits did you receive?

2. What does it mean that love demands an exchange? Discuss as a group.

3. How is this different from what popular culture tells us love is?

4. What is the deepest human need? What do we deserve?

5. How does Jesus' gift, his life for ours, affect you emotionally? Why?

6. Paul Miller writes, "If you take Jesus' gift, it means that God doesn't just love you; he enjoys and delights in you" (238). Is this love of God difficult for you to grasp? Why or why not?

7. If you answered yes to the previous question, personalize the statement with your name: "If _____ takes Jesus' gift, it means that God doesn't just love _____ ; he enjoys and delights in _____ ." Pray and ask God for faith to believe his Word instead of your feelings: "There is therefore now no condemnation for those who are in Christ Jesus" (Romans 8:1).

8. What did the Spirit help you see about either Jesus or yourself through this lesson?

Chapter 23

THE BIRTH OF HOPE

The End of Love's Journey

1. What does it mean that, without hope, love makes no sense? Discuss as a group.

2. Why is it significant that Jesus defeated death? Why is it important for love?

3. Jesus' resurrection body still has scars. In Paul Miller's words, "What a strange God, who doesn't remain aloof, but enters our world and becomes wounded" (245). What strikes you about that?

4. What significance for love does Paul draw from Jesus' scars (243-245)?

5. How does having the Spirit of Jesus empower us to love? How did it change the disciples?

6. Read Romans 5:3-5. How does the reality of these verses change the way we live?

7. What did the Spirit help you see about either Jesus or yourself through this lesson?

Chapter 24

OPENING THE DOOR

WHAT DO WE DO WITH JESUS?

1. Can you relate to Anne Lamott's story? In what ways is Jesus' pursuit of her reassuring to you?

2. How has Jesus found you in your deepest fears and met you in your smallest need? Share an example with the group as you feel comfortable.

3. How has your definition of love changed during this study? What are some of the major things you have learned about love? Discuss as a group.

4. How is Jesus' pattern of loving beginning to impact your relationships? Discuss as a group.

5. Jesus intrudes and invites; where do you need to respond to him?

6. What did the Spirit help you see about either Jesus or yourself through this lesson?

7. What have you learned in the fifth part of this book about how love moves through death into life? How is that impacting your life?

ABOUT THE
AUTHORS

Lydia Leggett, Seminar Coordinator for seeJesus, has enjoyed teaching *Person of Jesus* and *A Praying Life* in various groups for the last ten years. Even now, her women's Bible study group gathers for "tea and charts"—where they look at Jesus and love, and giggle at Lydia's drawings. When she's not coordinating seminars with churches throughout the U.S., she loves helping with publishing projects for seeJesus Press. Lydia has a B.A. in English from Trinity International University, and lives in southern Colorado with her husband.

Michele Bennett Walton leads seeJesus' publishing ministry, helping to produce resources that produce disciples. Having previously served various ministries in roles ranging from publicity and marketing to editing, Michele feels like she's finally found her place at seeJesus. Michele has a B.A. in Christian Ethics (Union University), a Masters in Church-State Studies (Baylor University), and lives in Upstate South Carolina, where she's learning from Jesus how to love her husband and three-year-old son.

About

seeJesus is a global discipling mission passionate about equipping the worldwide church to reflect all the beauty of Jesus. We invite you to learn more about our books, Bible studies, and seminars:

 Subscribe at info@seejesus.net

 Listen at seeJesus.net/podcast

 @_PaulEMiller

 Facebook/seeJesus.net